This book belong

Sophie McLean

Contents

My Little Book of
Nursery Rhymes

Brown Watson
ENGLAND

First published 2012 by Brown Watson
The Old Mill, 76 Fleckney Road,
Kibworth Beauchamp, Leic LE8 0HG

ISBN: 978-0-7097-1974-8

Humpty Dumpty

Humpty Dumpty sat on a wall,
Humpty Dumpty had a great fall.
All the King's horses
And all the King's men,
Couldn't put Humpty together again.

One, Two, Buckle My Shoe

One, two, buckle my shoe;

Three, four, knock at the door;

Five, six, pick up sticks;

Seven, eight, lay them straight;

Nine, ten, my fat hen;

Eleven, twelve, dig and delve;

Thirteen, fourteen, maids a-courting;

Fifteen, sixteen, maids in the kitchen;

Seventeen, eighteen, maids in waiting;

Nineteen, twenty, my plate's empty.

Jack and Jill

Jack and Jill went up the hill
To fetch a pail of water.
Jack fell down and broke his crown,
And Jill came tumbling after.

Up Jack got, and home did trot
As fast as he could caper;
He went to bed to mend his head
With vinegar and brown paper.

Old King Cole

Old King Cole was a merry old soul,
And a merry old soul was he;
He called for his pipe,
And he called for his bowl,
And he called for his fiddlers three.
Every fiddler had a fine fiddle,
And a very fine fiddle had he;
Oh, there's none so rare,
As can compare
With King Cole and his
Fiddlers three.

This Little Piggy

This little piggy went to market,
This little piggy stayed at home,
This little piggy had roast beef,
This little piggy had none,
And this little piggy cried,
"Wee, wee, wee,"
All the way home!

Polly Put the Kettle On

Polly put the kettle on,
Polly put the kettle on,
Polly put the kettle on,
We'll all have tea.

Sukey take it off again,
Sukey take it off again,
Sukey take it off again,
They've all gone away.

Little Bo-Peep

Little Bo-Peep has lost her sheep,
And doesn't know where to find them;
Leave them alone, and they'll come home,
Wagging their tails behind them.

Baa Baa Black Sheep

Baa baa black sheep, have you any wool?
Yes, sir, yes, sir, three bags full!
One for the master, one for the dame,
And one for the little boy who lives
Down the lane.

Here We Go Round the Mulberry Bush

Here we go round the mulberry bush,
The mulberry bush, the mulberry bush.
Here we go round the mulberry bush,
On a cold and frosty morning.

Boys and Girls, Come Out to Play

Boys and girls, come out to play,
The moon doth shine as bright as day.
Leave your supper and leave your sleep,
And come with your playfellows into the street.
Come with a whoop and come with a call,
Come with a good will, or not at all.
Up the ladder and down the wall,
A halfpenny loaf will serve us all;
You find the milk, and I'll find the flour,
And we'll have a pudding
In half-an-hour.

Horsey, Horsey

Horsey, horsey don't you stop,
Just let your feet go clippetty-clop.
The tail goes swish and the wheels go round
Giddy up, we're homeward bound.

I'm A Little Teapot

I'm a little teapot, short and stout,
Here's my handle, here's my spout.
When I see the teacups, hear me shout,
"Tip me up and pour me out!"

Wee Willie Winkie

Wee Willie Winkie runs through the town,
Upstairs and downstairs in his nightgown,
Rapping at the window and crying through the lock,
Are all the children in bed, it's past eight o'clock?

Incy Wincy Spider

Incy Wincy Spider climbed up the water spout.
Down came the rain and washed the spider out.
Out came the sun and dried up all the rain,
And Incy Wincy Spider climbed
Up the spout again!

Rub-a-Dub-Dub

Rub-a-dub-dub,
Three men in a tub,
And who do you think they be?
The butcher, the baker,
The candlestick-maker,
And up they jump all three!

Little Miss Muffet

Little Miss Muffet
Sat on a tuffet,
Eating her curds and whey;
Along came a spider,
Who sat down beside her,
And frightened Miss Muffet away.

There Was an Old Woman

There was an old woman who lived in a shoe,
She had so many children she didn't know what to do!
So she gave them some broth without any bread,
And she whipped them all soundly,
And sent them to bed!

The Queen of Hearts

The Queen of Hearts
She made some tarts,
All on a summer's day;
The Knave of Hearts,
He stole the tarts,
And took them right away.

The King of Hearts
Called for the tarts,
And beat the Knave full sore;
The Knave of Hearts
Brought back the tarts,
And vowed he'd steal no more.

The Grand Old Duke of York

Oh, the grand old Duke of York,

He had ten thousand men;

He marched them up to the top of the hill,

And he marched them down again.

When they were up, they were up,

And when they were down, they were down,
And when they were only halfway up,
They were neither up nor down.

Mary, Mary

Mary, Mary, quite contrary,
How does your garden grow?
With silver bells,
And cockle shells,
And pretty maids all in a row.

Hey Diddle, Diddle

Hey diddle, diddle,
The cat and the fiddle,
The cow jumped over the moon.

The little dog laughed
To see such sport,
And the dish ran away
With the spoon.